MUSICAL MOMENTS

Alto
Saxophone

Book 4

12 original compositions
& arrangements
for Alto Saxophone & Piano

Selected and edited by
Kirsty Hetherington

Published by
Trinity College London
Registered Office:
89 Albert Embankment
London SE1 7TP UK

T +44 (0)20 7820 6100
F +44 (0)20 7820 6161
E music@trinitycollege.co.uk
www.trinitycollege.co.uk

Registered in the UK
Company no. 02683033
Charity no. 1014792

Layout: Scott Barnard

Printed in England by Halstan & Co. Ltd, Amersham, Bucks.

Toreador's Song

From *Carmen*

arr. Patrick Gundry-White

Georges Bizet
(1838-1875)

Tambourin

from *Pièces de clavecin*, Suite in E minor

arr. Robin Hagues

Jean-Philippe Rameau
(1683-1764)

La Moreau

Andy Scott
(born 1966)

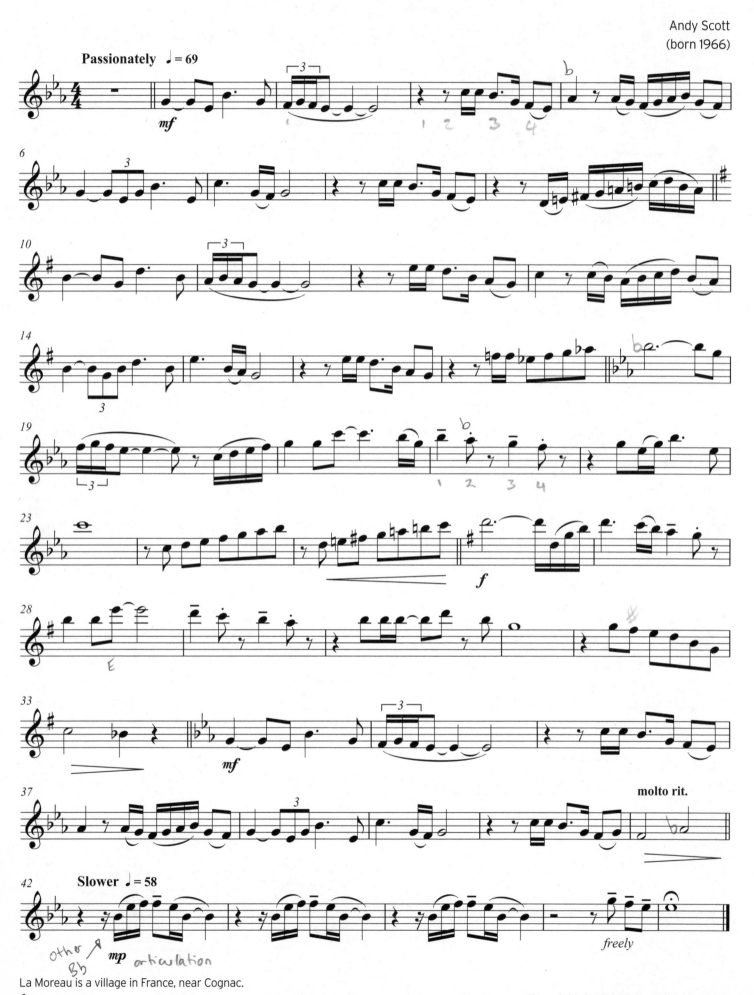

La Moreau is a village in France, near Cognac.

6

Scherzo

from String Quartet in E♭ ('The Joke'), Hob. III:38

arr. Andrew Challinger

Franz Joseph Haydn
(1732–1809)

Don't Look Back

Karen Street
(born 1959)

Berceuse

from *Jocelyn* op. 100

arr. Andrew Challinger

Benjamin Godard
(1849-1895)

Solveig's Song

arr. Robin Hagues

Edvard Grieg
(1843-1907)

Armando's Rhumba

arr. Andreas Panayi

Chick Corea
(born 1941)

Mexican Hat Dance

arr. Paul McClure

Traditional Mexican

16

Statement

Christopher Gunning
(born 1944)

17

OrangoTango

Rob Buckland
(born 1967)

Johnson Rag

arr. Andreas Panayi

Guy Hall & Henry Kleinkauf

* = lip bend